# BRAIN TEASERS

## Mind boggling pocket puzzles for kids!

ARCTURUS

ARCTURUS

This edition published in 2010 by Arcturus Publishing Limited
26/27 Bickels Yard, 151–153 Bermondsey Street,
London SE1 3HA

ISBN: 978-1-84837-633-5
CH001577EN

Illustrations by Andy Peters

Printed in India

# Contents

| | |
|---|---|
| Eye Tricks | 4 |
| Identical Pairs | 16 |
| Put Your Mind To It | 36 |
| Spot The Difference | 56 |
| Shadow Match | 76 |
| Secret Pictures | 96 |
| Answers | 107 |

# EYE TRICKS

## Cubing it

Are the black faces at the top or the bottom of the cubes?
Look closely and you'll see them both ways.

# Crazy Cat

This cat looks like it's sitting on a normal staircase.
But can you work out how it got up there?
The stairs are actually impossible to climb!

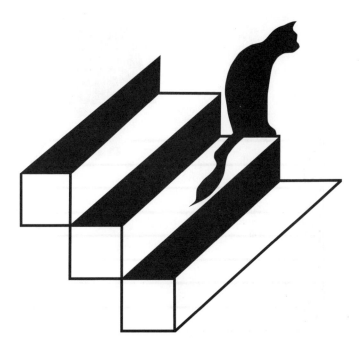

# Impossible Shelves

How many shelves can you see? Are you sure about the number? Count them again. Depending on how you look at the picture, you may see three shelves or four.

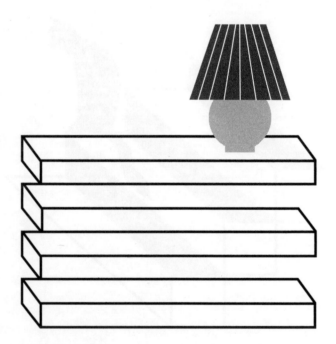

# Sausage Finger Trick

Follow the steps to create your own incredible
trick of the eye. Get your friends to try it too!

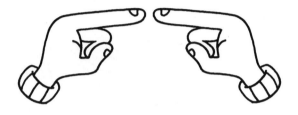

**1** Place your two index fingers together and bring them
level with your face so they're touching the tip of your nose.

**2** Now move your fingers away from your nose slowly
while looking past them. A floating sausage will appear
in front of your eyes.

# Perfect Circle?

Does this circle look a bit wonky to you?
Try tracing over it with a compass. You'll see
it's perfectly round. The lines behind the circle
are making it seem bent out of shape.

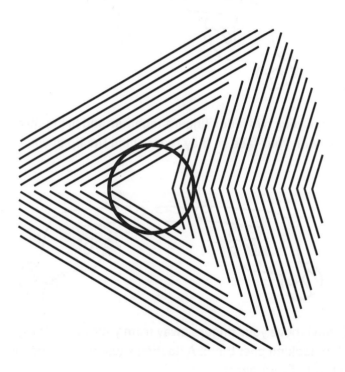

# Switch On The Lights

You'll need a separate white sheet of paper for this trick.
Stare at the lightbulb for 30 seconds, then look at the paper.
You'll turn on the lights and the bulb will glow white!

# Balancing Act

Is the balancing block level with the block underneath?
Measure the gap between them in two places.
Even though they don't look it, the two blocks
are parallel to one another.

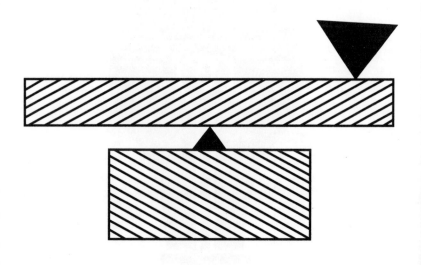

# Funny Fork

How many prongs can you see at the end of this fork?
It looks like three but the prongs don't make sense.
You wouldn't be able to eat your dinner
with a funny fork like this!

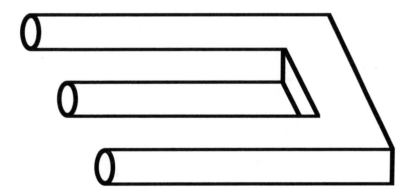

# Crazy Train Tracks

A train would have a hard time travelling along these tracks. Or would it? Even though these lines don't look parallel, they are. The crossing lines make them bend.

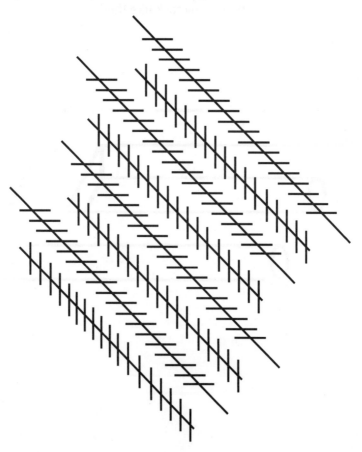

# Animal Magic

These magical animals can transform themselves.
What do you see? A swan or a squirrel?
A donkey or a seal?

# Never-ending Steps

Try climbing these steps. Can you reach the top?
If you do, what has happened to the bottom step?
A person who really climbed these steps would
be climbing forever.

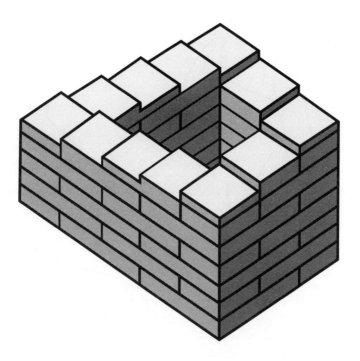

# Hole in Your Hand

Confuse your eyes and make a hole appear
in your hand as if by magic!

**1** Take a piece of paper
and roll it into a tube.

**2** Hold the tube up to one eye
while you cover your other
eye with your free hand.

**3** Keep both eyes open and
slowly move your free hand
away from your face along
the edge of the tube. A hole
will appear in your hand.

## Why does this happen?

The hole appears because although
your eyes see two different pictures,
your brain tries to make sense of them
and turns them into one picture.

## Cool Headgear

These baseball caps look the same but are they?
Only two are identical. Work out which two.

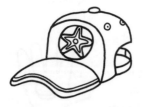 

# Crazy Chameleons

Which two crazy chameleons lounging
on the branches are identical?

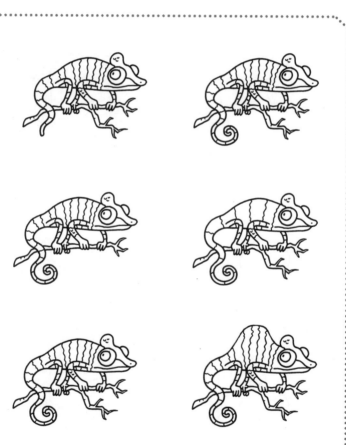

# Pack Your Sack

Two of these rucksacks are the same.
Can you work out which two?

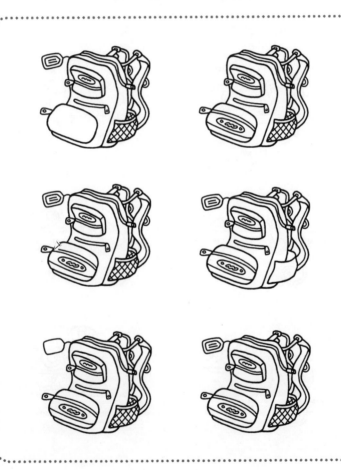

# Panda Snack

Which two of these munching pandas are
exactly the same as each other?

# Feeling Fruity

Can you spot which two juicy
fruit boxes are identical?

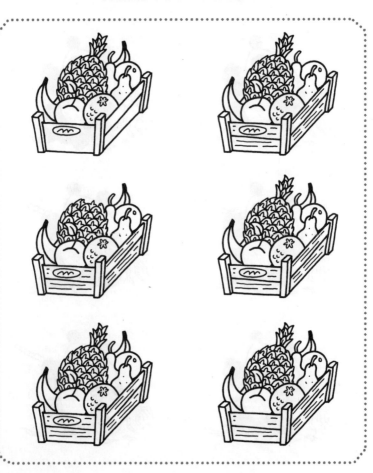

# Snap To it

These snapping crocodiles look the same but
are they? Only two match. Work out which two.

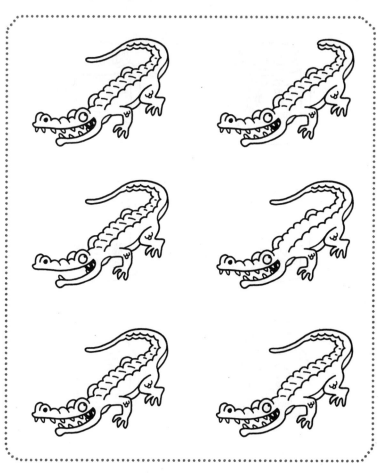

# Which Honey Pot?

Which two pots filled to the brim
with yummy honey are the same?

# Woof Woof!

Take a look at these funny spotty
dogs. Which two are identical?

# Yee-hah Hat!

These cowgirl hats look identical but they're not.
Only two are the same. Can you spot which two?

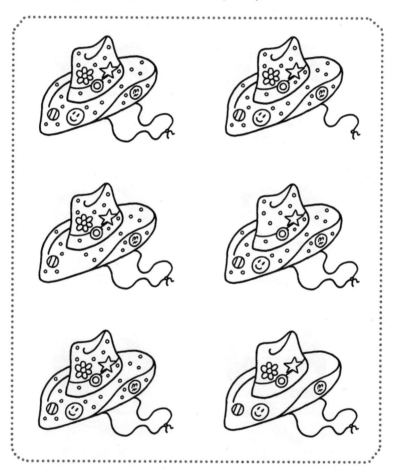

# Fabulous Fish

Which two fabulous fish are the same
as each other? Look closely to find out.

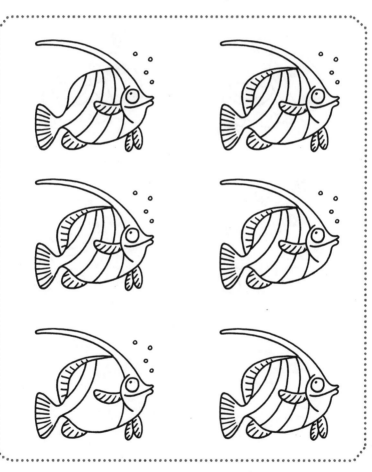

# Robot Dog

Take a look at these cute robot dogs.
Work out which two are the same.

# Weedy Seahorse

Two of these seahorses clinging to their
seaweed are identical. Can you tell which two?

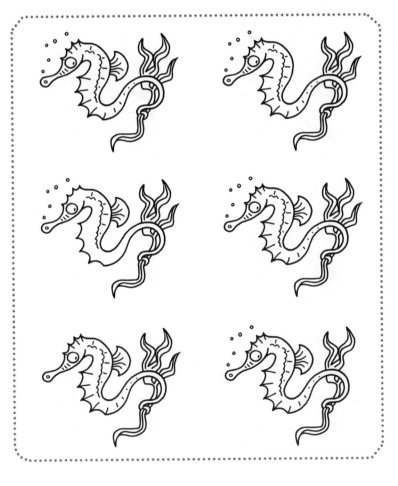

# Whooooooh!

Two of these spooky spirits are
the same. Can you spot which two?

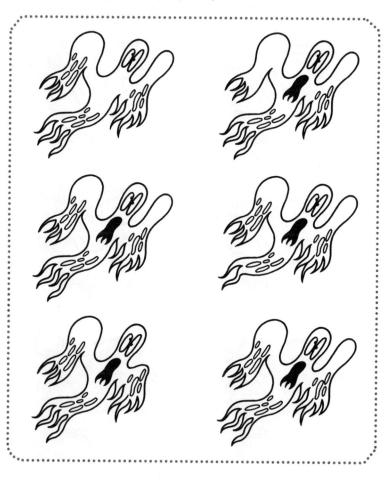

# Pick A Penguin

Which two penguins sheltering
their eggs are identical?

# Beady Bangle

These beaded bangles look similar but only two of them match. Decide which two they are.

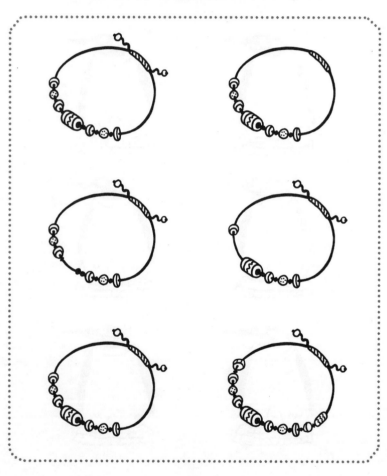

# Munch ... Munch!

These munching ladybirds are enjoying
their feast. Which two pictures are the same?

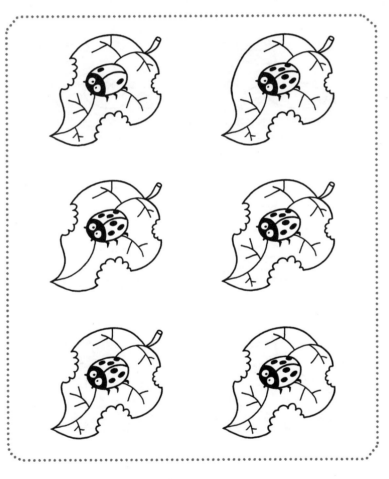

# Rolling Along

These hi-tech rollerblades will have you whizzing down the road. Which two pictures are identical?

# Beach Babe

The beach babe has left behind her mat and shades.
Which two pictures are the same?

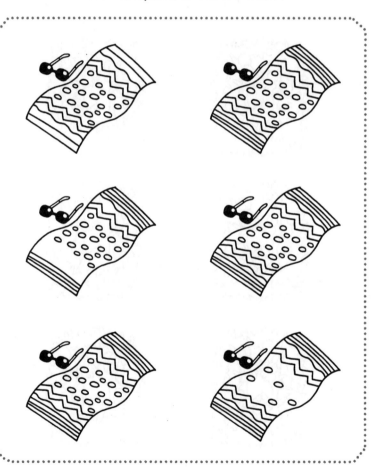

# Hungry Chicks

The hungry chicks are calling from their nest.
Can you spot which two nests are the same?

# Lacy Butterflies

Two of these lacy butterflies are
identical. Figure out which two they are.

# Planet Disaster

Oh no! The planets in our solar system have collided and broken apart. Match the word parts to put them back together. What three other space objects did you find?

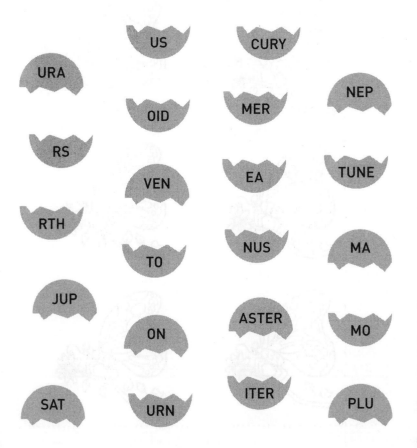

# Matchstick Squares

Try this tricky teaser. Change the four squares shown here into five squares by moving two matchsticks only.

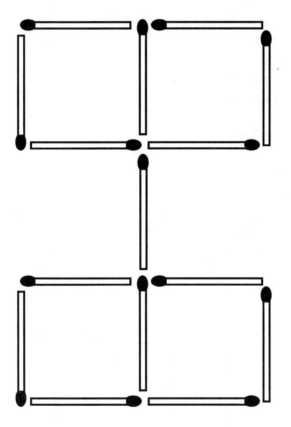

## ★ Teaser Tip

Take 15 matches and lay them out on a table. Then try doing the puzzle.

# Cool Camping

Louis is going camping this weekend. Can you work out how many of his mates are coming with him?

- It's more than 3 but fewer than 20
- It's not 10
- It's not an odd number
- It can't be divided by 3
- It's not a multiple of 4

## ★ Teaser Tip

Write down all the numbers from 1–20,
then cross them out as you work out the clues.

# All Squared Up

How many squares can you count? Think carefully!

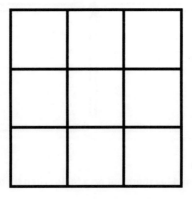

# What's The Word?

Read the sign. Can you spot what's wrong with the phrase? If you can't, try again and look at each word separately.

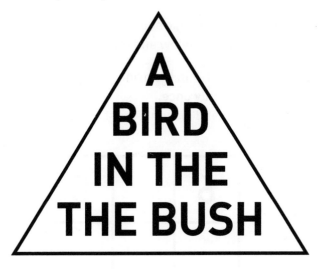

A
BIRD
IN THE
THE BUSH

# Cute Cat Story

Once a siamese cat named Nelly lived in a house. There were three other cats in the house. Their names were Bertie, Bingo and Margot. What do you think the fourth cat's name was?

# Magic Square (Bronze)

People have been amazed by magic squares since ancient times. In a magic square, the numbers in each row, column and diagonal always add up to the same number.

Can you complete this magic square?
Follow the instructions below and give it a go.

• Write the numbers 1-9 in the grid.
• Use each number only once.
• Each row, column and diagonal must add up to 15.

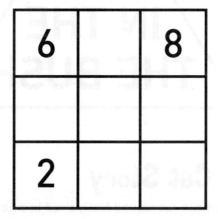

★ **Teaser Tip**
Write down the numbers from 1-9 on a separate sheet of paper and cross them off as you put them on the grid.

# Letter Ladders

Make your way down the ladders by changing only one letter in the word above to make a new word.

If you get stuck or end up with too many words, you can use the clues to help but try without first!

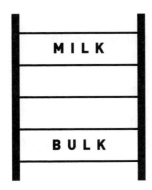

**M I L K**

**B U L K**

## Clues
- A type of soft material
- People in a bad mood do this

## Clues
- When you can't find something
- You're at the back of the pack

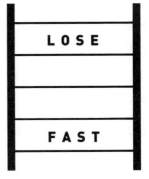

**L O S E**

**F A S T**

## ★ Teaser Tip
Look for letters that appear at both the top and the bottom of the ladder. Your words will always contain them.

# Mental Mindreading Trick

Try out this incredible number trick on yourself.
We can guarantee you will be amazed!

**1** Pick a number between 1 and 10.

**2** Multiply the number by 9.

**3** Add the digits of the number you made in step two together.

**4** Subtract 5 from the new number.

**5** Find a letter in the alphabet that matches the number you made in step four, e.g. 1 = A, 2 = B, etc.

**6** Pick a country that starts with that letter.

**7** Choose an animal that starts with the last letter of your country.

**8** Pick a colour that starts with the last letter of your animal.

**9** What's your answer? Now turn to page 113.

## ★ Teaser Tip

Try this trick on your mates.
Tell them you're a mindreader and give them the answer!

# Pieces of Pie

Can you work out which number is missing from the last piece of pie?

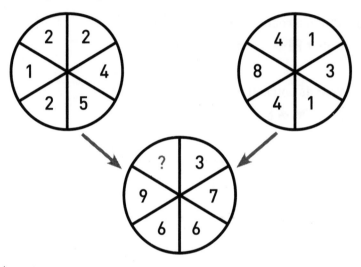

★ **Teaser Tip**
Study the matching segments in each pie and write them down in order. Then work out the pattern.

# Mystery Twins

Two baby girls were born on the same day in the same year with the same mother and father, but they are not twins.

Can you explain how this can be?

# It's No Joke!

Use the codebuster to work out the punchlines
to these jokes and give yourself a laugh.

**Q**: What's a robot's favourite food?

**A**: ✦ ✤ ◆ ■ ♣   ◆ ★ ✤ □ ❖

**Q**: What do you call a cowboy with no legs?

**A**: ✪   ▼ ♣ ◗   ☆ ♣ ◗ ✳   ❄ ✳ ✦

**Q**: What did the duck say when it bought some lipstick?

**A**: □ ✳ ○   ✤ ○   ♣ ✳   ✦ ❀   ❄ ✤ ▼ ▼

**Q**: Why was the crab arrested?

**A**: ★ ♥   ◗ ✪ ❖   ✪ ▼ ◗ ✪ ❀ ❖
□ ✤ ✳ ◆ ★ ✤ ✳ ✿   ○ ★ ✤ ✳ ✿ ❖

---

## Codebuster

| A | B | C | D | E | F | G | H | I | J | K | L | M |
|---|---|---|---|---|---|---|---|---|---|---|---|---|
| ✪ | ❄ | ◆ | ☆ | ♥ | ✳ | ✿ | ★ | ✤ | ▲ | ✖ | ▼ | ✦ |

| N | O | P | Q | R | S | T | U | V | W | X | Y | Z |
|---|---|---|---|---|---|---|---|---|---|---|---|---|
| ✳ | ♣ | □ | ✓ | ■ | ❖ | ○ | ✳ | ❃ | ◗ | ◐ | ❀ | ✚ |

# Matchstick Triangles

Bend your brain around this puzzle. Change the nine equal triangles shown here into five triangles by removing five matchsticks.

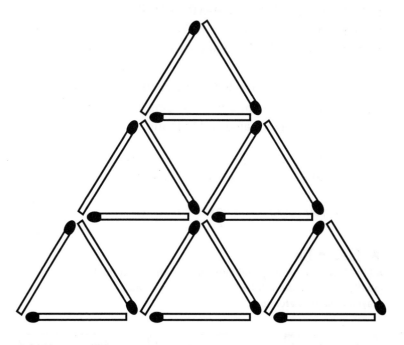

## ★ Teaser Tip

Try this puzzle out with real sticks and experiment with different positions.

# Box Mix-Up

You've been asked to help sort out a big mix-up.
In front of you are three boxes.

• The first box is labelled MAYONNAISE.
• The second box is labelled KETCHUP.
• The third box is labelled MAYONNAISE & KETCHUP.

None of the boxes are labelled correctly but one does contain mayonnaise, another contains ketchup and one has both mayonnaise and ketchup.

The only thing you're allowed to do is to reach into one box, take out a sachet, and look at it?

How can you relabel the boxes correctly?

## ★ Teaser Tip
All the boxes are wrongly labelled, so you know that the box labelled MAYONNAISE & KETCHUP can only contain either mayonnaise OR ketchup.

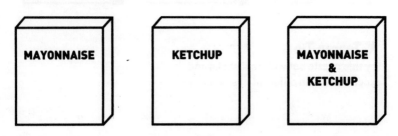

# Magic Square (Silver)

Did you manage to complete the magic square on page 40? If so, it's time to step up a gear!

- Write the numbers 1-16 in the grid.
- Use each number only once.
- Each row, column and diagonal must add up to 34.

| 2 | 15 |    | 9  |
|---|----|----|----|
|   |    | 13 |    |
|   | 5  |    |    |
| 7 |    |    | 16 |

## ★ Teaser Tip
Tackle the rows, columns or diagonals with the most numbers in them first.

# Jumbled Tags

Unjumble the letters to discover what musical gifts are attached to the tags.

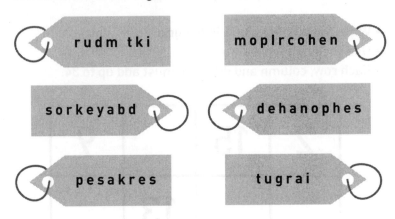

rudm tki

moplrcohen

sorkeyabd

dehanophes

pesakres

tugrai

# Hidden Birds

Can you find a bird hiding in each of these sentences?

Jane was speaking French awkwardly.

The flea gleefully jumped on to the cat.

There was a painful throb in his arm.

"How long do we have to wait for the bus?" she asked.

# Clever Coins

You will need 3 copper and 2 silver coins.
Arrange them in this pattern:

Now, try to make this pattern:

You can make only 3 moves and you must move
2 coins next to each other at a time. Can you do it?

# Mighty Muffins

Amelia and Grace are making muffins for a party.
Work out out how much money they need to spend.

| RECIPE | COST |
|--------|------|
| 9 eggs | 1 egg = 30p |
| 1.5 kg flour | 1 kg flour = £1.10 |
| 200 g cocoa | 100 g cocoa = £1.30 |
| 275 g butter | 100 g butter = 80p |
| 275 g sugar | 100 g sugar = 20p |

# They're Bugging Me!

The bugs are all on the loose! Match the word parts together to find the name of 12 creepy critters.

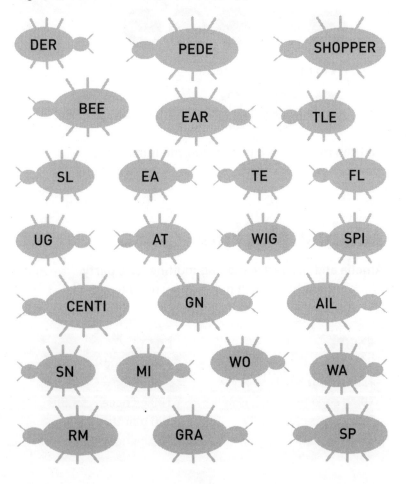

DER

PEDE

SHOPPER

BEE

EAR

TLE

SL

EA

TE

FL

UG

AT

WIG

SPI

CENTI

GN

AIL

SN

MI

WO

WA

RM

GRA

SP

# Got The Wrong Number?

Which number shouldn't be in each of these stars?

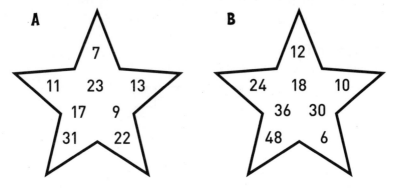

**A**

7
11  23  13
17  9
31  22

**B**

12
24  18  10
36  30
48  6

★ **Teaser Tip**

Look for a different number pattern in each star.

# Loopy Line-Up

A group of kids are standing in a row. Work out the fewest number of kids there can be in the row.

A girl is to the left of a boy.
A boy is to the left of a boy.
Two boys are to the right of a girl.

★ **Teaser Tip**

Draw a diagram. The answer is not 4.

# Brick By Brick

Jeremy and Mike can build a wall 5 bricks long and 5 bricks high in 1 minute. How long will it take them to build a wall 10 bricks long and 10 bricks high?

★ **Teaser Tip**
Draw a diagram of the finished wall to help you.

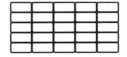

# Tricky Triangle

How many triangles can you count in this shape?

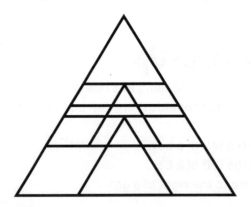

★ **Teaser Tip**
Look closely. There are more than 6.

# Magic Square (Diamond)

Go for broke and try to complete this super-hard magic square!

- Write the numbers 1-24 in the grid.
- Use each number only once.
- Each row, column and diagonal must add up to 65.

| 25 | 16 |    |    |    |
|----|----|----|----|----|
| 1  |    | 20 | 17 | 21 |
|    | 22 | 14 |    | 7  |
|    |    |    |    |    |
|    | 13 | 12 | 23 | 2  |

★ **Teaser Tip**

Check your answers when you complete a row or column.
Write down the different sum combinations.

# What's Your Age?

Here's a great number trick to play on someone if you want to find out how old they are. Try it on yourself first!

**1** Choose a number between 1 and 9. Write it down.

**2** Multiply the number by 2.

**3** Add 5 to this number.

**4** Now multiply the number by 50.

**5** If you haven't had your birthday, add 1758 to the number. If you've had your birthday add 1759 to the number.

**6** Subtract the year you were born, e.g. 1998.

**7** You should get the number you first thought of followed by your age!

# Mystery Creature

Cross out the letters that appear more than once. Then unscramble the leftover letters to discover a legendary creature.

P   N   G   U     H   T   M   I

H   S   V     E   D   P   X   E   V

    I   U     O

X   R   M   T   A   S

# Puzzling Pyramid

Every number on the upper level of the pyramid is the sum of the two numbers below it, e.g. 11 + 7 = 18. Can you climb to the top?

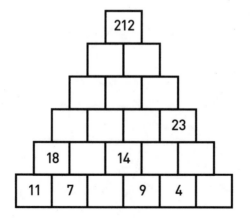

# SPOT THE DiFFERENCE

## Whizzing Along

It's crowded out on the ski slopes today! Can you can spot eight differences between the two pictures?

# Wacky Museum Tour

Take a tour around this wonderfully weird museum of past times. Look for eight differences between the two pictures.

# Loony Lab

This scientist's lab is packed with all kinds of crazy gadgets. Find eight differences between the two pictures.

# Arctic Adventure

The penguins are chilling on the ice. Can you spot eight differences between these two Arctic scenes?

# Let's Get Moving

Everyone is outdoors getting active in the park.
Find eight differences between the two scenes.

# Bedroom Glitz

This cowgirl's bedroom is full of glitz and glamour.
Find eight differences between the two pictures.

# Watery World

Dive into this wobbly watery world and see if you can spot eight differences between the two pictures.

# Jungle Hangout

The animals are having fun hanging out in the rainforest.
Look for eight differences between the two scenes.

# Spooky Graveyard

Whoooh! Find eight differences between the
two spooky graveyards if you dare.

# Alien Planet

The bouncing astronaut has some aliens to keep him company! Find eight differences between the two scenes.

# SHADOW MATCH

## Monkey Magic

Look closely at the curly-tailed monkey.
Only one shadow matches it. Which one is it?

# Majestic Castle

Which shadow matches the picture
of the majestic medieval castle?

# Funky Guitar

Find the shadow that matches the funky guitar.
Then play yourself a crazy solo!

# Sneaky Salamander

Which shadow matches the salamander sneaking across the page?

# Beautiful Blooms

Look closely at the beautiful blooms. Only one shadow matches the picture exactly. Which one is it?

# Fiery Dragon

Which shadow matches the picture
of the fire-breathing dragon?

# Moose On The Loose

Uh-oh! There's a wild moose on the loose.
Find the shadow that matches it.

# Magical Lamp

Here's a shiny magic lamp to rub and make
a wish. Which shadow matches it exactly?

# Which Keys?

Look closely at the bunch of keys. Only one shadow matches the picture. Which one is it?

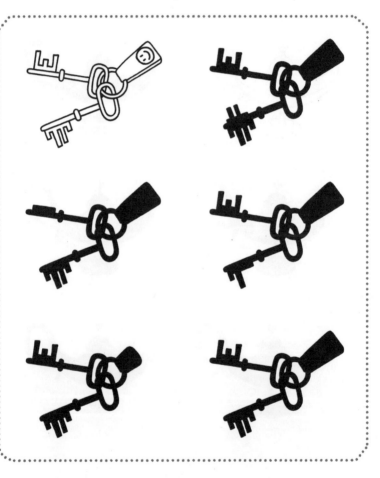

# Take A Bite

Which shadow matches the ferocious
wide-mouthed shark ready to take a bite?

# Palm Beach

Find the shadow that matches the desert island.
Then take a rest under the palm tree!

# Tou-Can Do it!

Only one of these shadows matches the toucan
sitting on a branch. Which one is it?

# Moth Match

Which shadow is the same as the
patterned moth fluttering across the page?

# Sky Diving

This daredevil man has parachuted from the sky!
Which shadow matches him exactly?

# Precious Stones

Look closely at the pretty necklace. Only one shadow is the same. Which one is it?

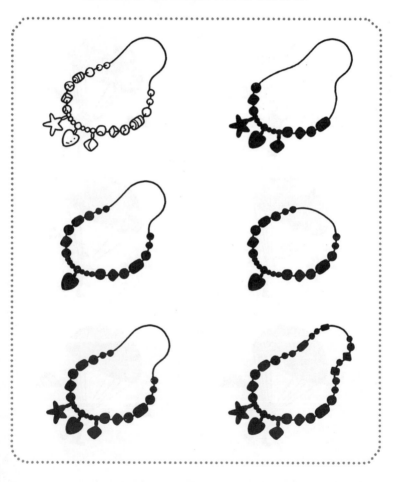

# Spiky Stegosaurus

Which shadow matches the picture
of the spiky stegosaurus?

# Prickly Pear

Ouch! Watch out for that prickly pear in the pot.
Which shadow matches it exactly?

# Boing ... Boing!

Can you spot which shadow matches
the bouncing kangaroo?

# Flying High

Look closely at the kite in the sky.
Only one shadow is the same. Which one is it?

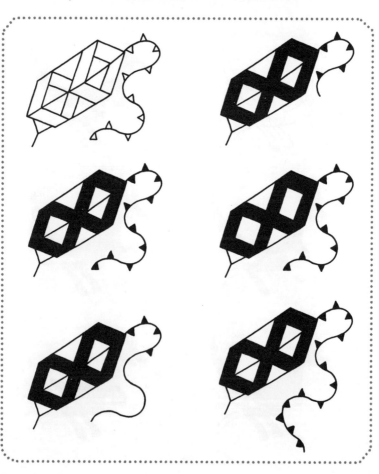

# Pampered Pooch

This pampered poodle is ready for the dog show!
Which shadow matches it exactly?

# SECRET PiCTURES

## That's Weird!

When you first look at the bizarre pictures in this section, you might wonder they are doing in this book! However, there is more to them than meets the eye. Each one contains an amazing 3D image. Below are some ways to help you see them.

## Push and Pull

1 Hold the page at a normal distance from your face.
2 Now relax your eyes and try not to focus.
3 Bring the page slowly to your face and let it blur.
4 Then slowly move the page away, still not focusing.
5 Repeat until the 3D image appears.

## Look Past

1 Hold the book in front of you and relax your eyes.
2 Let your focus go behind the page, as if you are looking through the page at a spot behind it.
3 Hold this focus until the 3D image appears.

Once you've mastered seeing one picture, it gets much easier. So keep on trying – it's worth it!

**TIP**
Don't give yourself eyestrain – take a break! Sometimes, the best way to see these pictures is when you're not trying too hard.

# Darting Dragonfly

A lace-winged dragonfly is darting across the pond.
Can you make it zoom towards you?

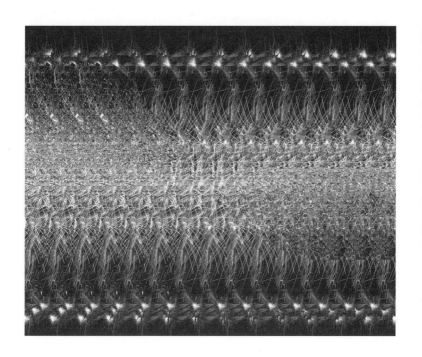

# In A Heartbeat

Can you see the beating heart and make
it go 3D? Keep on trying!

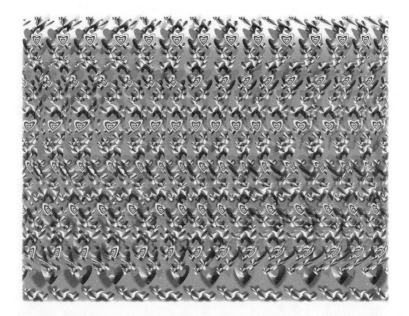

# Dancing Dinosaurs

Study the picture to discover
which two dinosaurs might be dancing.

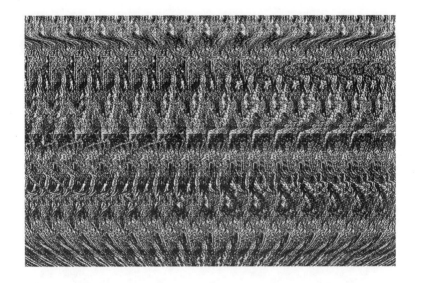

# Secret Symbol

Look at this picture to make a mysterious
magic bat-like symbol appear.

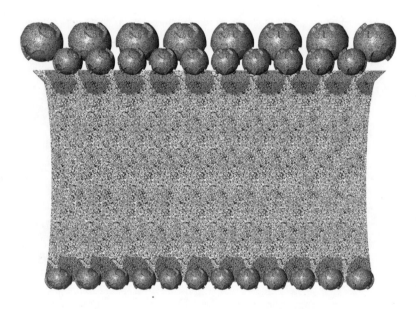

# Flutter and Wow!

What insect is hiding in this strange picture?
Relax your eyes and it might flutter towards you!

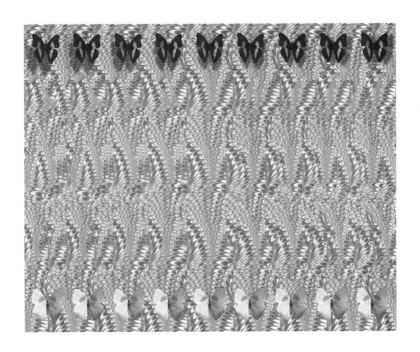

# Rings of Saturn

Want to see the rings of planet Saturn? Then feast your eyes on this incredible 3D experience.

# Making Honey

Hidden in the honeycomb are two busy bees.
Make them fly out of the waxy cells.

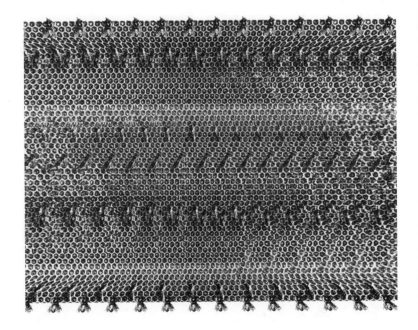

# Beautiful Cranes

Hiding in this picture are two long-legged cranes.
See if you can make them walk towards you.

# Crazy Clown Face

Study this picture to give yourself an eyeful.
Is the clown's face creepy or cute? You decide!

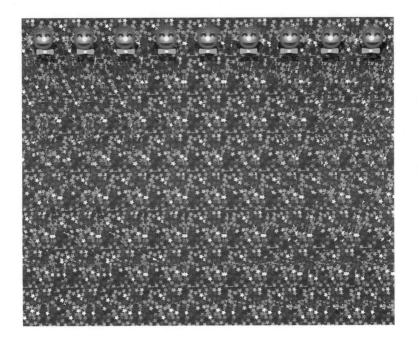

# Skull and Crossbones

Relax your eyes and wait for this scary pirate's skull and crossbones to pop out at you.

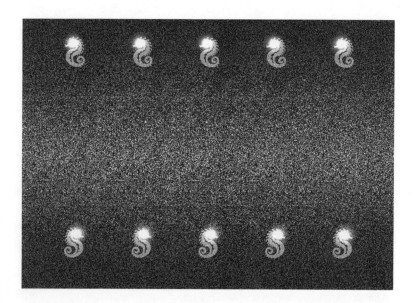

# ANSWERS

## iDENTiCAL PAiRS

### Page 16

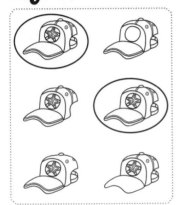

### Page 17

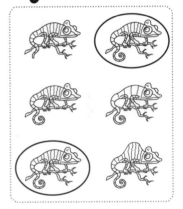

### Page 18

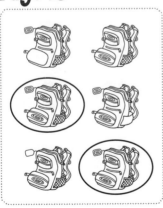

### Page 19

# Page 20

# Page 21

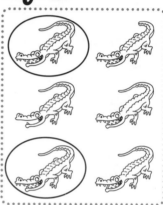

# Page 22

# Page 23

## Page 24

## Page 25

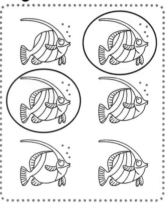

## Page 26

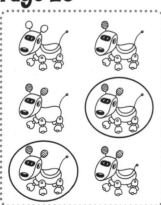

## Page 27

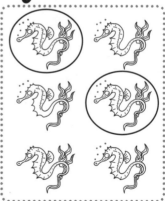

## Page 28

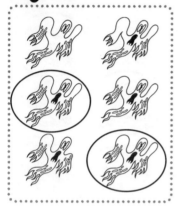

## Page 29

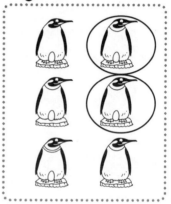

## Page 30

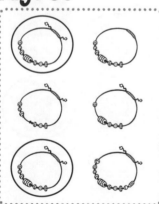

## Page 31

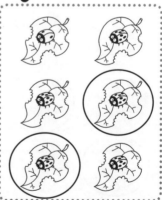

## Page 32

## Page 33

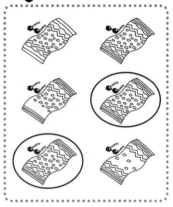

## Page 34

## Page 35

# PUT YOUR MIND TO IT

## Page 36 Planet Disaster

The planets are: Mercury    Venus    Earth    Mars
              Jupiter    Saturn    Uranus    Neptune

The other three space objects are an asteroid, the dwarf planet Pluto and the Moon.

## Page 37 Matchstick Squares

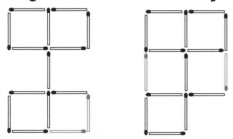

## Page 38 Cool Camping

There are 14 people going camping with Louis.

## Page 38 All Squared Up

There are 14 squares:

9 x small          4 x medium          1 x large

# Page 39 What's the Word?

Did you notice that the word 'the' is repeated twice in the sign? It's easy to miss when you're reading because your eyes jump over words but if you look at each word separately, you should spot it.

# Page 39 Cute Cat Story

The name of the fourth cat is Nelly. If there are three other cats in the house, then she must be the fourth cat!

# Page 40 Magic Square (Bronze)

| 6 | 1 | 8 |
|---|---|---|
| 7 | 5 | 3 |
| 2 | 9 | 4 |

# Page 41 Letter Ladders

| MILK |
|------|
| SILK |
| SULK |
| BULK |

| LOSE |
|------|
| LOST |
| LAST |
| FAST |

# Page 42 Mental Mindreading Trick

Did you get 'an orange kangaroo in Denmark'?
Nearly everyone does!

# Page 43 Pieces of Pie

The missing number is 6. The number in the third piece of pie is the sum of the two numbers in the other matching pieces, so 2 + 4 = 6.

# Page 43 Mystery Twins

The two baby girls are from a set of triplets.

# Page 44 it's No Joke!

The punchlines to the jokes are:

**Q**: What's a robot's favourite food?
**A**: Micro chips

**Q**: What do you call a cowboy with no legs?
**A**: A low-down bum

**Q**: What did the duck say when it bought some lipstick?
**A**: Put it on my bill

**Q**: Why was the crab arrested?
**A**: He was always pinching things

# Page 45 Matchstick Triangles

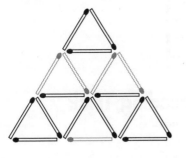
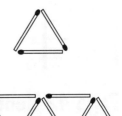

# Page 46 Box Mix-Up

Here's what to do to relabel the boxes correctly:

Look inside the box labelled MAYONNAISE & KETCHUP. You know this label is wrong, so if you pull out a sachet of ketchup, this must be the ketchup box.

The box labelled MAYONNAISE cannot contain mayonnaise because it's wrongly labelled. It also can't contain ketchup because you've used that label, so it must contain mayonnaise and ketchup.

The final box labelled KETCHUP is also labelled wrongly, so it can't contain ketchup. It must contain mayonnaise because that's the only free label left.

# Page 47 Magic Square (Silver)

| 2 | 15 | 8 | 9 |
|---|----|----|----|
| 14 | 4 | 13 | 3 |
| 11 | 5 | 12 | 6 |
| 7 | 10 | 1 | 16 |

# Page 48 Jumbled Tags

Drum kit, microphone, keyboards, headphones, speakers, guitar

# Page 48 Hidden Birds

Jane was speaking Fren**ch awk**wardly.

The fl**ea gle**efully jumped on to the cat.

There was a painful th**rob in** his arm.

"H**ow l**ong do we have to wait for the bus?" she asked.

# Page 49 Clever Coins

The three moves are:

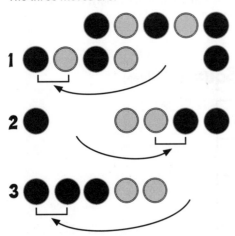

# Page 49 Mighty Muffins

Eggs = £2.70
Flour = £1.65
Cocoa = £2.60
Butter = £2.20
Sugar = 55p

The total cost of the muffins is £9.70

# Page 50 They're Bugging Me!

The bugs are: Beetle    Grasshopper    Centipede
Gnat    Snail    Earwig
Flea    Wasp    Worm
Slug    Spider    Mite

# Page 51 Got The Wrong number?

**A**: 22 is the wrong number. All the others are odd numbers.
**B**: 10 is the wrong number. All the others are multiples of 6.

# Page 51 Loopy Line-up

The fewest number of kids is 3: Girl  Boy  Boy

The answer is not 4 because there are two boys to the right of the girl, so one of those boys can be to the left of the other boy.

# Page 52 Brick By Brick

A 5 x 5 brick wall has 25 bricks, but a 10 x 10 brick wall has 100 bricks – that's 4 times as many. So, it will take them 4 times as long to build the 10 x 10 brick wall, making the answer 4 minutes.

# Page 52 Tricky Triangle

There are 10 triangles in total.

# Page 53 Magic Square (Diamond)

| 25 | 16 | 9 | 4 | 11 |
|----|----|----|----|----|
| 1 | 6 | 20 | 17 | 21 |
| 19 | 22 | 14 | 3 | 7 |
| 5 | 8 | 10 | 18 | 24 |
| 15 | 13 | 12 | 23 | 2 |

# Page 54 What's Your Age?

If you do the maths correctly, you'll get the number you first thought of followed by your age. E.g. 412. So in this example, the age is 12.

# Page 55 Mystery Creature

The answer is a dragon.

# Page 55 Puzzling Pyramid

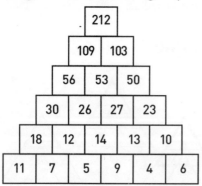

# SPOT THE DiFFERENCE

## Page 56

## Page 58

## Page 60

## Page 62

## Page 64

## Page 66

## Page 68

## Page 70

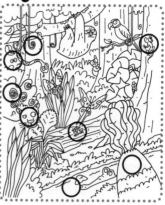

## Page 72

## Page 74

# SHADOW MATCH

## Page 76

## Page 77

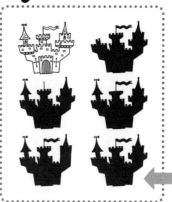

## Page 78

## Page 79

## Page 80

## Page 81

## Page 82

## Page 83

## Page 84

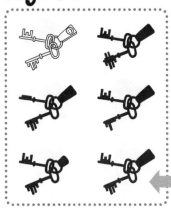

## Page 85

# Page 86

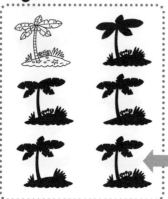

# Page 87

# Page 88

# Page 89

# Page 90

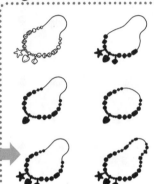

# Page 91

# Page 92

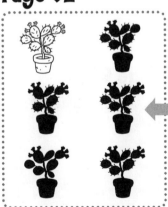

# Page 93

## Page 94

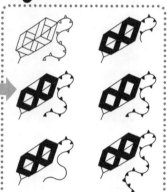

## Page 95

# SECRET PiCTURES

## Page 97

## Page 98

## Page 99

## Page 100

## Page 101

## Page 102

## Page 103

## Page 104

## Page 105

## Page 106